D1097717

★ THE GOLDEN COCKEREL ★

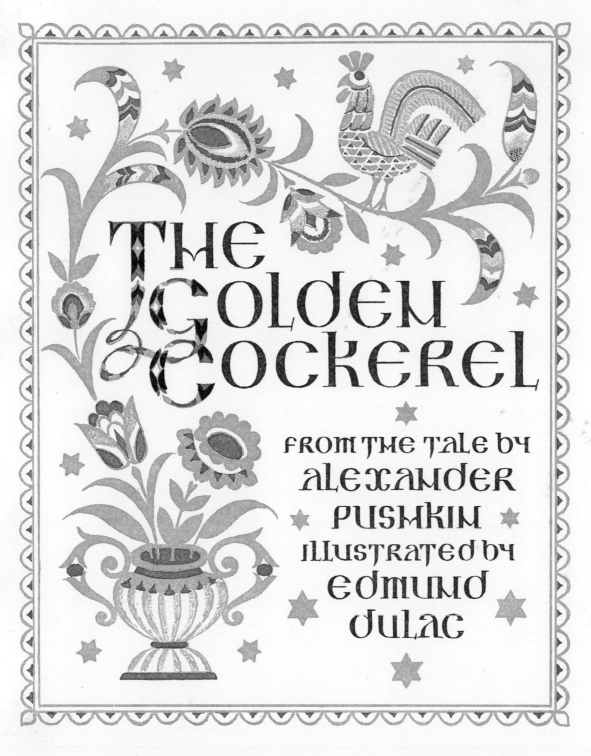

THE GOLDEN COCKEREL

FROM THE TALE BY
ALEXANDER
PUSHKIN
ILLUSTRATED BY
EDMUND
DULAC

★ ★ THE HERITAGE PRESS ★ ★ NEW YORK ★

A ✳ FOREWORD ✳

FTER NICHOLAS I, the newly crowned Tsar of Russia, had suppressed the revolutionary rising of December 1825, Alexander Pushkin, who had shown sympathy with the movement but had influential friends at Court, was granted an audience. He was forgiven. When he had gone, Nicholas said to his Secretary of State, Count Bludov: "I have been conversing with the wittiest man in Russia." With Pushkin's death Russia lost not only her "wittiest man" but also one of her best poets and a writer who was among the first to lay the foundations of modern Russian literature and to gather together some of the best stories and popular songs from the immense treasure of Russian folklore.

He was born at Moscow on the 7th of June, 1799, and came from an ancient family of Boyars. Early in life he acquired from his father, who was an agreeable poet, a fervent admiration for French literature and began writing poetry when he was still at the recently founded college of Tsarkoe Selo. On leaving the college in 1817 he was given a post in the Foreign Office. One of his best-known poems, *Ruslan and Ludmilla,* was written while he was there and also an *Ode to Liberty* inspired by the enthusiasm for liberal ideas that was, later, to get him into trouble on more than one occasion. The Ode was circulated in manuscript throughout St. Petersbourg. For such a daring act, a holiday in Siberia was the current reward, but

9

Pushkin was lucky and always managed to extricate himself from difficulties of this sort. This time he was merely sent in disgrace to Southern Russia. The beautiful scenery had a profound effect on his imagination; he wrote there his longest and best poems.

But it was during a period of self-imposed exile in the province of Pskov, after resigning his post on account of another political indiscretion, that his taste for folk tales and folk songs began to develop. On this occasion he spent two years on his mother's estate in the village of Mikhailovskoe with nothing to do but write, go for rides and in the evening "loll on the stove and listen to the old tales and the old songs." He grew passionately interested in everything that came from the people. His old nurse, Arina Rodionovna, who knew hundreds of tales and who had a special talent for telling and miming them, had much to do with it. She kept house for him in Mikhailovskoe and helped, no doubt, "to make good" what, in a letter to his brother, he calls "the deficiencies in my damnable education." Sometimes he would dress as a peasant and go to fairs or religious festivals, mixing with the people and picking up stories and old songs. Collecting tales became his absorbing passion to such an extent that he could not resist adding to those he gleaned quite a number that were of his own invention. These were so like the real thing that they deceived even experts. They now pass as genuine folk tales.

In spite of a certain Byronic influence in his poetry, he was perhaps the first writer to be characteristically Russian, and it was only natural that, later on, when Russian composers turned for melodic inspiration to the music of their own people, they should find in Pushkin's poems and stories an ideal source of dramatic subjects. One need only mention *Eugene Onyegin, Boris Godunov, The Queen of Spades, Tsar Saltan* and *The Golden Cockerel*. His reputation was becoming solidly established when, in 1837, he quarrelled with his brother-in-law, Baron George Heckeren d'Anthes, a foppish young man whom he had accused on very slender grounds of having designs on his wife. They fought a duel. Pushkin was wounded and died two days after on the 10th of February.

The "Tale of the Golden Cockerel" was written as a short poem in 1834. The tale appears to be a genuine *skazka*. Many elements in it are present in other Russian tales and point to an Eastern origin. The meaning of the tale is not easily explained. It no doubt belongs to the class of folk tales that start as clear and simple myths and, passing from one country to another, have other myths or incidents, often irrelevant, added to them from generation to generation in order to make them more entertaining. Pushkin's poem being rather short for a book, a little elaboration was found necessary. The librettist of Rimsky-Korsakov's opera took far greater liberties with it than have been taken here. Pushkin himself did not invent the story, and, if apologies are needed, who knows but that they should not be made to the spirit of his old nurse, Arina Rodionovna?

✶ THE GOLDEN COCKEREL ✶

THE GOLDEN COCKEREL

ONCE UPON A TIME, a very long time ago, in a Wonderland Kingdom, there lived a King. His name was Dodon. In his youth he had been a mighty warrior and fought many great battles against the King of the North and the King of the East and the King of the West and had beaten them all. And if there had been a King of the South he would have fought him also and beaten him. But in the South there was the sea. Sometimes, however, his enemies from the East and from the North came by way of the Southern Sea and tried to land on his shores. But King Dodon had a powerful fleet and always sank all their ships. And as years went by they ended by believing he was invincible. They no longer dared attack him and went in great fear of him.

So King Dodon lived in peace and the older he grew the more he liked peace. The thought of battle filled him with weariness and he wished for nothing but quiet and happy days with good food and

15

wine and to go to sleep to the sound of sweet music attended by his servant maids, who spread soft furs over his bed in winter and fanned the flies away in summer. He had been a skilful general and brave as a lion, and it was with him as it is with lions when they are growing old. His enemies said: "He has lost his teeth and his claws are broken." And little by little they became bolder. Once again they gathered their armies and began to march across the borders of his kingdom, pillaging and setting towns and villages on fire. There was no more peace for King Dodon. Dark clouds cast a shadow upon the serenity of his days. His nights were full of alarms. All joy departed from his life. He lost his taste for food and wine and sweet music. Neither had his generals any rest. Once again they were rushing their soldiers from one end of the country to the other. If they kept watch upon the East, the invaders came in from the West, and if they watched the North they came in from the sea. King Dodon cursed and swore. He would have torn out his hair, but with age the curly locks of his youth had become scant and the top of his head was bald and shiny like an egg. So he tore his beard and cried: "What an ill wind has blown away my peace! I have no rest. I cannot sleep at ease. My life has become one long misery. Will no one help me? How can any one help me?" And which-

ever way he turned there was indeed no help. Several times a day he called together his ministers. They were old and as wise as ministers can be, but they could think of no way to put an end to his troubles. They took counsel from every side, offered rewards, threatened punishments, but all in vain.

A T LAST, one day, King Dodon's Nurse, who was by now very old, remembered that when she was a girl, there lived in a remote part of the kingdom, a famous Astrologer who was also a Magician. People said he could read the future in the stars, perform every sort of incantation, command every sort of spirit, contrive every sort of talisman to pro-tect against peril, and give life to things that had none. Perhaps he was still alive, perhaps he would know of a means to ward off all danger in the future and make King Dodon's life happy and quiet again. So the Old Nurse told King Dodon of her thoughts next morning as she was bringing him his breakfast. And he smiled as he had not smiled for a long time. He put his arms round her neck and kissed her on both cheeks. "You always were a clever woman," he said, and on the instant called his Grand Seneschal and asked him to tell the Court Chamberlain to instruct the Ordinator of Speedy Tidings to send messengers in search of the Astrologer. No sooner, however, had the messengers set out than there was a noise at the Palace Gates. King Dodon looked out and saw in the courtyard a crowd of people watching with great interest a very ancient-looking man who

17

had suddenly appeared from nowhere. He was bent with age, he was thin and pale and had a long white beard. He was dressed in a long black robe embroidered with mysterious designs; on his head he wore a long white pointed hat, and he carried a long wand in his hand and a bag over his shoulder. "There he is!" cried the Nurse, who was also at the window. "Go and tell him to come up," said the King. When the Old Magician entered the Royal Bedroom, King Dodon was sitting up in bed gaping with wonder and expectation. "Well!" he exclaimed. "You are indeed the most exalted among Astrologers, the most transcendent of Magicians, what can you do for me?" "Noble King, Lord among the lords," replied the Very Old Man, "I was waiting for you to call me. I know your distress and it is my greatest wish that your mind should

18

The older Dodon grew, the more he liked peace

find peace again. I have with me a cure for all your troubles." He opened his bag, took out a Cockerel made of gold and laid it in front of the King. "This bird," he went on, "is a magic bird. Set him on the highest pinnacle of the highest spire in the town. He will watch over you and your people by day and by night and will warn you of all attacks coming from the land or from the sea. You will be able once more to sleep and rest to your heart's content. As long as quiet reigns in the Kingdom, the bird will be silent. But if the country is threatened, he will flap his wings and crow loudly, turning towards the quarter from where the danger is coming." As he was speaking, the Cockerel stood up, flapped his wings and cried: "Cock-a-doodle-doo! Your Majesty may sleep in peace!" King Dodon's face was shining with delight, his fat body was shaking with joy. He lifted his hands. "Marvel of Marvels!" he shouted. "Blessings upon this miraculous bird! As for you, most sublime of Magicians, I will give you a hundred sacks of gold." "I do not care for gold," said the Very Old Man. "I can make it myself when I need it." "Then I shall make you my Supreme Minister." And the Very Old Man said: "Honours are nothing to me." "Well!" insisted the King. "What do you want as a reward? Ask what you wish and I promise on my oath that it shall

21

be granted." The Old Astrologer smiled faintly and with his long fingers stroked his long white beard. "I will remember your promise, noble King," he replied and at once vanished out of sight. When King Dodon had sufficiently recovered from his astonishment, he ordered the Cockerel to be set up on the highest spire in the town. But the town was full of spires, turrets, domes and cupolas, and the Superintendent of Public Buildings did not remember which was the highest of them. They had all to be carefully measured as instructions about magic talismans have to be followed to the letter. As it happened, the highest spire was found to be in the very centre of the Capital, near the Royal Palace, so that everyone was able to see the bird from every street and every square in the City. The bird was set on its topmost pinnacle. At the slightest sign of danger he would flap his wings, turn to the North or the West or maybe to the East and cry: "Cock-a-doodle-doo!" And the enemy approaching the frontiers would turn and run. Then, high above the town, the Golden Bird would cry again: "Cock-a-doodle-doo! Your Majesty may sleep in peace!" After a while, finding that they could no longer take King Dodon by surprise, the neighbouring kings lost heart. Their attacks became less frequent and in the end they ceased altogether. Quiet again reigned over the land and over the sea and again King Dodon settled down to a calm and sweet life, lying in bed and enjoying his food, his wine, his music and his sleep. And the years went by and the Golden Cockerel was almost forgotten, when, one night, King Dodon was

The Cockerel causes Dodon to shake with joy

awakened by a great noise. The servants and the guards were running to and fro in the Palace, and outside the people had gathered near the gates shouting: "Wake up! little Father, wake up! We are in danger!" King Dodon sat up, yawned and rubbed his eyes. "What is all this noise?" he said, and the Grand Seneschal, who had rushed into the Bedroom, replied: "O King, the whole town is up and about, the Golden Cockerel is crowing!" "Is he?" said King Dodon. "I was fast asleep. I didn't hear him." He got up and opened the window. Against the deep blue sky the golden bird was flapping his wings and crowing at the top of his voice in the direction of the East. King Dodon yawned again, swore and called his eldest son. "You heard the warning, my son. The enemy is at the Eastern posts, curse him! There is no time to lose!" So the eldest son called the generals, the generals called the captains and the captains gathered their troops and they all set out towards the East. And when the last echo of the last trumpet had died and the last soldier had passed the City gates, the Golden Cockerel folded his wings and resumed his quiet watch. And King Dodon went to sleep again.

SIX TIMES the sun rose and set, the moon waned slowly to her last quarter and no messenger had yet come from the battle front. Everywhere people were asking "Is there any news?" The answer was ever the same. "No, there is no news." And they went about their work hoping the morning would bring tidings. But the morning brought no tidings. Night came, and suddenly the silence was broken. High above the City the Golden Cockerel was flapping his wings and crowing "Cock-a-doodle-doo!" And still he was turned towards the East. King Dodon sat up, yawned and rubbed his eyes. He looked out of the window. "What does it all mean?" he moaned. "From the East again? Then my army must be in danger. It may be destroyed at this hour. What can I do?" This time there was great alarm in the Palace. Seneschal, Chamberlain, ministers and officers rushed into the Royal Bedroom. King Dodon called his second son. "Your brother and his army seemed to be in peril, my son. Gather your men and fly to their rescue." The younger son called the generals, the generals called the captains and the captains assembled their troops and they all marched towards the East. The Golden Cockerel folded his wings and resumed his quiet watch. And King Dodon went to sleep again. Days went by, another week passed. No messenger came from the battle front. The people went about in silence; they hardly dared ask if anyone had heard anything. In the Palace everybody spoke in whispers, saying: "The King is worried. In

the old days, news came from the battle front every day and sometimes twice a day. Every time it was the news of a victory, but now
there is no news at all. It is very strange." They spoke truly. King
Dodon was restless. For a fortnight there had been fighting in the
East and no one knew how it was going on. Neither Seneschal,
Chamberlain, ministers nor even the Old Nurse could offer any
good reason for this long silence. Some were of opinion that the
enemy had been beaten and had retreated so fast and so far that no
messenger could be sent in time. Some said it might be that it was
the King's army that had been beaten, that all the soldiers were dead
and there was no messenger to send. The Old Nurse believed there
was no enemy at all and that the Cockerel had made a mistake, or
that something had gone wrong with him. But all this was no help
to King Dodon. For three days he had hardly touched his food and
his wine and he had not called for his musicians. He slept badly

and, for the first time in his life, he had nightmares. Indeed he was wide awake when, for the third time, the Golden Cockerel flapped his wings and crowed "Cock-a-doodle-doo!" still pointing towards the East. "Well!" said King Dodon sadly. "My two sons have gone and have not returned. I am no longer young, but I think I can fight again. Moreover there is no one to lead the rest of my soldiers. So I will go myself." And he called for the Keeper of the Household Oddments and asked for his armour. Twelve valets brought him his coat of mail, his breastplate, his helmet, his buckler and his sword. He had grown fat and the armour had become a little tight. But the valets tugged on one side and the maids pulled on the other and in the end they succeeded in fitting it on him. Then he called his generals, the generals called the captains and the captains called their troops and with King Dodon at their head they all marched towards the East.

They marched through the towns and villages. They marched through the valleys and over the hills, they crossed many fields and waded through many streams. For a whole week they marched and nowhere could they see a sign of battle. Every little while scouts went ahead, but they would come back to say that they had seen no trace of the fighting or any vestige of the two armies. King Dodon

would scratch his bald head and stroke his beard and say "This is a very odd thing indeed!" And they went on marching. At the end of another week they reached the foot of the mountains and, as they were coming down the side of a hill, they found themselves in a green valley that was so well hidden that no one could have known of its existence. King Dodon came down from his horse and looked round. The valley was full of trees and lovely flowers and there was not a sound to be heard anywhere. There seemed to be no birds, no living creature in it at all. Nothing save the trees and lovely flowers. King Dodon was wondering at the mysterious silence with some perplexity when his heart leapt in his breast. He had caught sight of a large tent that, he was almost sure, was not there when he first entered the valley. It stood in the middle of it where the most graceful trees and the brightest flowers grew, and it was made of rich embroidered silk and adorned with coloured banners. He ordered his troops to be on their guard and, with cautious steps, advanced towards it. Alas! his perplexity was soon changed to dismay as he became aware of the desolation surrounding him. On all sides, to the right and to the left of his path, on the green grass among the lovely flowers, lay the dead bodies of his warriors, generals, captains, archers, horsemen and all. And the strange thing was that not a single enemy

could be seen among them. "How can this be?" exclaimed King Dodon. "What invisible foes were they fighting? Not a single enemy dead can be seen among them!" As he approached the tent, dismay gave way to utter consternation. At his feet his two sons were lying lifeless. They had taken off their helmets and their armour; side by side they had fallen. Each had still his brother's sword plunged deep in his heart. Their horses were running free and wild over the bloodstained grass among the trees. How was it King Dodon had seen none of this before? He lifted his hands to heaven, large tears were flowing down his beard. "Oh! my sons, my little falcons, Death has caught you in her net, her cold 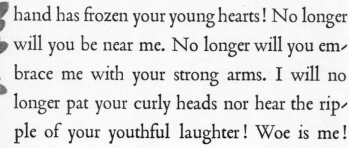 hand has frozen your young hearts! No longer will you be near me. No longer will you embrace me with your strong arms. I will no longer pat your curly heads nor hear the ripple of your youthful laughter! Woe is me!

30

She was like a lily among many-coloured flowers

My life has come to an end. Death is waiting for me!" And, as he sobbed, the mysterious silence of the valley was suddenly broken. Behind him the generals, the captains and the soldiers sobbed and lamented with him. The trees moaned, the flowers wept aloud and a dismal wailing rose from the hills round. And as King Dodon raised his head and wiped his eyes, the curtains of the tent opened and against the darkness, like a shaft of light, stood a young woman radiantly beautiful. She was surrounded by her maids and was like a burning lily among many-coloured flowers. King Dodon was struck dumb. He stared like a night-bird dazzled by the sun. The young woman stepped forward, smiling and stretching out her hands, and said: "In the name of the Mirror of All Splendours, Dispenser of Enchantments, in the name of the Light of the Morning and the Shimmering Stars, I, the Queen of Shemakhan greet you King Dodon. I knew you would come to me and I made all things ready to receive you in my tent. Here in this quiet valley I will give you peace and every pleasure. My maids will bring to your table rare delicacies and refreshing wines. As days follow days your eyes will see only things of delight, your ears will hear only pleasant sounds and your heart will be young again. All this is by my wish, and it may be that your dreams are coming true or it

may be that this valley and your dead sons and your dead soldiers who fought in vain to conquer me are still a dream." She spoke, and King Dodon gazed at the young Queen. He forgot his dead sons, his dead generals, his dead soldiers, he forgot he had a kingdom. And he took the hand of the Queen of Shemakhan and together they entered the tent. Days followed days. The hours passed and King Dodon lost count of them. Round the tent of the Queen of Shemakhan the green valley had become an enchanting garden. The lovely flowers were disposed in beds of harmonious colours. There were groves of trees bearing fruit of rare and delicate flavour that glowed like gems among the leaves. All round, winding paths and alleys were spread with fine yellow sand and here and there adorned with fountains that whispered soothingly and ponds where golden and ruby fish darted in and out through the tangle of waterlilies. And in this restful place King Dodon tasted every delight. He enjoyed delectable dishes and exquisite wines. For the pleasure of his eyes, maids danced for him dances that were like the gliding of sails on a calm sea. His ears were caressed by music designed to gladden the heart or give the mind repose. There were slaves skilled as storytellers to recite to him fables and legends and entertain him with whimsical tales. And all the while he lay under the spell of the beautiful Queen, bewitched by the magic of her long dark eyes, entranced by the perfume of her black hair, enraptured by the softness of her silvery voice that was like the twittering of birds at dawn.

34

SOMEONE has said: folly is a fault in youth and in age a madness and it will ever make a man see wonders. As time went on, King Dodon grew more besotted and more foolish. His generals, who had endeavoured to while away the long hours by playing games and hunting wild beasts, were becoming weary and impatient. At last they thought he had feasted and taken his pleasure long enough. They wanted to see their homes, their wives and their children again, and they went to King Dodon and spoke to him. But they said nothing of all this. Instead, they bowed to the ground very respectfully and reminded him that he had a Kingdom and a people who needed his care and his guidance and that without doubt everyone in the Capital was anxiously waiting for him to return. And when it was decided that the Queen of Shemakhan should come back with him, as his bride, King Dodon said he was ready to depart. And so they started on their journey. The vanguard with the heralds carrying banners and pennons and the drummers and the trumpeters went first, followed by the painted Chariot, in which the Queen of Shemakhan sat with King Dodon, and the generals on their horses, some riding in front and some behind. Then came the archers, the pikemen, the horsemen and the rest of the army with the captains and the officers, sword in hand. They went by the high roads and through many towns and villages. And, as they passed, the people came out singing songs of welcome and bringing presents. After they had travelled many days they reached the Capital. There were great crowds at the gates and great crowds in the streets cheering, singing, throwing flowers and bowing low as King Dodon went by. And in front of the Royal Palace, the multitude was so large that the clamour of the cheering was like the roar of great waves breaking upon the rocks. "Welcome! little Father, welcome to you and your Bride!" shouted the people and many cries of praise and many blessings. King Dodon waved his hand right and left, and the Queen of Shemakhan smiled and fluttered her scarf with a grace that was irresistible. But as the procession came to a standstill, suddenly a hush fell upon the crowds. Paler, thinner and more bent than ever a Very Old Man with a long white beard, dressed in a long black robe and with a long white hat upon his head, was advancing with small steps towards the Royal Chariot. Again he seemed to have

36

appeared from nowhere. King Dodon saw him and leaned out. "Ah! my old friend!" he cried. "This is a day of gladness and I rejoice that you should be here. Come near and tell me what you came for." "Noble King," replied the Very Old Man. "A long time ago when I gave you the Golden Cockerel, you offered me in return wonderful gifts, but I asked you only to grant me the first request I should make, and this you solemnly promised to do." "Well!" said King Dodon. "Tell me what it is you wish and if it is within my power you shall have it." "My wish," said the Magician, "is that you give me your beautiful bride, the Queen of Shemakhan." For a moment King Dodon was dumbfounded. Then he became annoyed: "How can you make such a request? Are you possessed of evil spirits or has your mind turned mouldy with age? You do not know what you are asking of me." "Only to fulfil your promise," answered the Old Man. And King Dodon was embarrassed and angry. "It is true I promised," he said like one who is about to blow hot and cold with his words. "But many years have gone since, and no promise can bind a man for ever. Likewise no one can be expected to grant a wish when it is not in his power to do so. And to give you my bride, the Queen of Shemakhan, would be far beyond my power." "The word of a King should be imperishable as a diamond," the Magician said quietly. King Dodon became flushed with passion. "You drivelling old babbler!" he cried. "You are so old that you can no longer count your years. How can you think of wanting a young maiden,

37

a beautiful young maiden like the Queen of Shemakhan, when I would give you more gold and precious stones than a hundred slaves can carry, or the richest province of my Kingdom, or even my horse?'' The Old Astrologer shook his head. ''I care for none of these things. I said  so to you long ago. Now I care only for the young Queen of Shemakhan.'' King Dodon flew into a rage. ''May the Evil Spirits blister your tongue and dry up your spleen. If you will not listen to reason then you shall have nothing from me. Never let

 your foolish face offend my eyes again. Begone! or I shall have you beaten till you howl for mercy! Begone! while your skin and your bones are still unbroken!'' But no threats could deter the Very Old Man. He went on arguing, pointing with one finger and hitting the ground with his long wand, till King Dodon could contain himself no more. He spat and swore: ''By the

"The Cockerel has left his perch!"

Lord of Calamities, I will put an end to your cackle!" And he raised his sceptre, which was a heavy one, and struck the Magician on the head. The Old Man fell. Whether he was dead or not no one could say for he could nowhere be found. The Queen of Shemakhan thought the whole scene diverting to the extreme. She could not stop laughing, and her body quivered with mirth like a young aspen in the breeze. King Dodon, on the other hand, was very troubled. His face was red and his beard was ruffled and his mind was sore. But he had only to look at his lovely bride as he sat back, and all his anger died down like the black wind of night that turns away before the rising sun. He smiled and wagged his head at her and was about to step down from the Chariot, when there came, from above, a strange sound like a rushing of dead leaves in a storm. Everyone looked up. A great shout rose from the crowd: "The Cockerel has left his perch!" And indeed the Golden Bird was no longer standing on his pinnacle high above the City, he was flying across the blue sky, flying down fast towards the Royal Chariot. He hovered for an instant above King Dodon, crowing "Cock-a-doodle-doo!" then like an arrow dropped upon his head. And he pecked, pecked, pecked him right on the top of his bald head. Not enough, you would have thought, to do more than scratch the skin, but King Dodon gave a long sigh and fell all of a heap. Whether he was dead or not no one could say, for here ends the tale. As for the Queen of Shemakhan, she had vanished and was never seen again.

41

ND THAT IS ALL there is to tell about King Dodon and the Queen of Shemakhan. It may be King Dodon, his sons and his soldiers never died, or it may be they came to life again, and it is said that both the Old Astrologer and the Queen of Shemakhan are still alive among the living. Indeed this would not be incredible as they are the only real people in the Story. And in all this you may read any meaning you please, for dreams and fancies can live for a time and life is perhaps only a dream.